The Wise Bear Stories
Helping you through life's journey

How to love the things you don't

Scott Cranfield

Illustration Raphilena Bonito

The Wise Bear Stories
How to love the things you don't
Scott Cranfield

ISBN 9781912821044

A CIP catalogue record for this book
is available from the British Library.A CIP catalogue record for this book
is available from the British Library.

Published 2019
Tricorn Books
Aspex Gallery, 42 The Vulcan Building
Gunwharf Quays
Portsmouth PO1 3BF

Printed & bound in the UK

The Wise Bear Stories

How to love the things you don't

How it Started:

Scott Cranfield the Author of Wise Bear has coached at the highest level for over 30 years, appearing on TV, radio, magazines, as well as hosting multiple seminars and being a key note speaker. His coaching covers subjects from life coaching and family relationships, to sport and business.

Since a young age I have been fascinated with and studied ways to help myself and others live the most inspired and fulfilled life possible. My journey has involved travelling the World attending countless programs and courses covering just about every area of life with the World's leading teachers.

As a father I wanted to share the best of what I had learnt with my children. I found a very effective way of doing this was through bedtime stories. I would create stories involving the challenges and anxieties my children had experienced that day and at the centre of each story is a character called Wise Bear. During the story the children would share with Wise Bear what was upsetting them or causing them to feel anxious. Wise Bear would use his vast experience and wisdom and share a whole new way of looking at these concerns to bring a calming balance to the children's mind, a balance they couldn't find on their own.

In each story the children learn useful tools and actions they can then apply for the rest of their lives.

My whole family are involved in bringing these stories to life, and it is our wish that these stories now help many other children and families, in the way they have helped ours.

Who is Wise Bear:

Wise Bear has been in the same family for generations. He has developed a unique wisdom that allows him to guide children, helping them dissolve their anxieties, as well as helping them make sense of the

different challenges and events they experience in their lives.
Every story covers a different subject, but within each story Wise Bear offers timeless lessons and vital life skills to help children navigate the journey of their life.

The lessons from Wise Bear will bring a calming balance to your children's mind, and give them a new and empowering perspective on any anxieties or challenges they face.

Even at 100 years old Wise Bear is still fascinated to learn and develop himself. He has had many brilliant teachers along the way, one special one he affectionately refers to as Dr D.

Wise Bear loves to read, exercise, make healthy smoothies and meditate. The only thing that gives away his age are some of his quirky sayings!

More than a story:
Each story ends with an affirmation and a short exercise to reinforce the lesson you have been reading about. This is a great opportunity to work with your children and help them apply the lessons directly to their own life.

Affirmations are a powerful way to develop strong and empowering beliefs for children, and the exercises give the children the opportunity to work through some of the challenges they face, so they can dissolve the anxieties and negative effects they hold in their mind.

How to love the things you don't

It was Saturday morning and Toby was in the kitchen trying to do his maths homework. He was fidgeting and finding it hard to focus. Football training was on in half an hour and he wanted to pull on his boots and get on the pitch. This was leading to mistakes in his maths homework.

"Do you think that there are more leaves in the world or blades of grass?" Toby asked no one in particular.

"Do birds have dreams?" he added.

The page of maths homework looked woefully unfinished, apart from an interesting doodle of a dog with wellies on.

Wise Bear was standing in the kitchen, sipping a peppermint tea. He noticed Toby daydreaming and getting distracted from his maths. Toby got up to get his third glass of water in 20 minutes.

H e was doing anything to avoid doing maths.

Wise Bear caught Toby's eye.

"How are you getting on with your maths homework?" he asked, knowingly.

"Um, what do you think, Wise Bear? Blades or leaves?"

Wise Bear gazed at Toby with his large green eyes.

Toby frowned.

"It's so tough! I really can't concentrate. Maths is so difficult and boring for me. My teacher says I don't concentrate and that I have got ants in my pants."

Wise Bear stifled a chuckle. But he thought he could help Toby.

"Toby, come and sit down with me and I will give you some ideas on how to concentrate better."

"I haven't got time for that!" said Toby, panicking. "I'm running late as it is!"

Toby grabbed the papers in front of him and shuffled them around, causing a couple of sheets to fall to the floor.

Wise Bear reached down and picked them up for him. Handing them back to him, he spoke.

"Toby, this chat will only take a few minutes and once you understand it, you will be able to work faster. Do you want to hear it?"

"OK, can we make it quick please?" Toby said, a sense of urgency in his voice.

Wise Bear encouraged Toby to come with him to sit on the sofa. Then he began.

"Toby, your mind works in a very interesting way."

Wise Bear paused to make sure Toby was listening.

"When something is important to you, your focus and concentration will be strong. And yet when you are trying to do something that is not important to you, your mind will jump around, and you will lose focus."

Toby looked a little worried, so Wise Bear reassured him.

"Don't worry, Toby. I'm not talking about just you. This is true for everybody. For example, your maths teacher is probably completely focused when teaching maths, but I'm certain there will be some things in her life that she struggles to concentrate on. That's not good or bad, just the truth that some things are more important to us than other things and this affects our concentration."

Toby wasn't sure that he believed Wise Bear on this occasion.

"But I do know maths is important. And I still can't concentrate."

"Well, how do you know maths is important?" asked Wise Bear.

"Because Mum and Dad told me, plus my school teachers are always telling me it is," Toby whined.

Wise Bear could see that his lesson would be of great benefit to Toby.

"Ah, but having others tell you it's important, is not the same as you finding out for yourself! And until you can do that, Toby, you may not concentrate at your best."

Toby put his head on one side and glared at Wise Bear. He needed this to be helpful, otherwise he wouldn't get his homework done AND he'd be late for football practice.

"Toby, what are you doing when your concentration and focus is sharp and comes naturally?"

Toby responded energetically, "Playing football and watching football. Even playing football on my computer game."

Toby really liked football.

Wise Bear then asked, "Toby have you ever considered how being good at maths will help you with your football?"

Toby couldn't believe his ears. He laughed so hard he almost rolled off the sofa onto the floor.

"Wise Bear, have you ever watched football? Maths won't help me with football!" he said, continuing to chuckle.

"Well, golly gosh, old bean!" replied Wise Bear. "Of course I have watched football and I also know that being good at maths will help you with your football."

Wise Bear spoke with a stern voice, which made Toby sit up and pay attention.

"Toby, there are times when you need to do things that won't seem important to you or that simply seem too difficult. When this happens you can either continue to struggle with these things or you can change the way you look at them which may help you get a better result. Would you be interested in learning how to do that?" Wise Bear said firmly.

"You will need to give me an example, as I am not sure I understand," said Toby, suddenly quieter.

"Of course," responded Wise Bear. "What do your parents say about eating your vegetables if you want a pudding?"

"Well Mum always says that if you want your ice cream after dinner you need to eat up all your vegetables."

"And what usually happens?" asked Wise Bear.

"If I know I'm going to get ice cream, then of course I always eat my vegetables up!"

"Exactly!" confirmed Wise Bear. "You see it is important to Mum that you are healthy, so she wants you to eat the vegetables. And when you know the way to get the ice cream is to eat the vegetables, you will tend to stay focused and eat them."

Toby laughed again and said, "Yes that's very true."

"So, let's get back to maths… If you can find out how

getting better at maths will help you with football, you will have more energy and focus to do your maths."

Wise Bear now had Toby's full attention. He continued and repeated his earlier question.

"Toby, how will getting better at maths help your football?"

Toby still looked blank, so Wise Bear helped him out.

"Let's think about a football field, Toby. What shape is it?"

"Well it's sort of rectangular," responded Toby.

"Yes that's right. And what else on the football field is rectangular?"

"Well now you mention it, quite a few things," said Toby, suddenly enjoying this lesson. "There is the six-yard box, the penalty area and even the goal is like a rectangle."

Toby was even surprising himself now.

"And isn't a rectangle two squares joined together?" Wise Bear asked.

"Yes!" said Toby, who was now realising there was more maths in football than he first thought.

"What other shapes are there on the football pitch?" Wise Bear asked.

"Well of course there are circles for the penalty spot and the centre spot plus the centre circle and even the corner area is an arc." Toby was imagining the football pitch in his head.

"Splendid!" said Wise Bear.

"And isn't there a small section of circle adjoining the penalty area?"

"Wow, you really do know a bit about football!" teased Toby, grinning from ear to ear.

Wise Bear continued, "Aren't there angles on the football pitch where the different lines meet?"

"Yes! That's right!" said Toby.

Wise Bear was pleased that he had caught Toby's imagination.

"Now think about when the players are passing the ball to each other or shooting at goal – they are at different angles to each other, so there is maths here."

Toby was now surprised as well as interested in what Wise Bear was saying.

"In fact, Toby," Wise Bear continued, "it seems there is a lot of maths in football."

Toby paused and stared at the ceiling, thinking about all the angles and shapes in football.

"Yes, I suppose there is," said Toby. "I have never seen it that way before."

Wise Bear knew there was more, so he carried on.

"Let's look at kicking a football," he said. "To change the height of your shot or make the ball curve, do you have to change the angle of your foot and leg when you kick the ball?"

Toby was now getting quite interested and thought about that question for a moment. Nodding enthusiastically, he said, "Yes, yes! I think you're right! I could change the spin on the ball by changing the angle I kick the ball at."

"Well once again isn't all of that linked to maths?" hinted Wise Bear.

"Wow, I never realised there was so much maths involved in football!" said Toby, shaking his head in disbelief.

"And don't forget about time, Toby! For example, how long is each half of the game? Add on extra time and injury time. All of these can be worked out as either fractions or percentages. If there was three minutes of injury time added to the game, what percentage increase would that be?"

Toby took a big breath and started muttering numbers to himself. Wise Bear chuckled, clapping his paws together.

"Don't worry, old bean," he said. "I just wanted to show you an example of where maths can get interesting for football. Some of the answers might even help you develop a new mindset with football.

"I am sure the more you understand maths and relate it to every aspect of football, the more it could help you get better at football, whether that's playing on a pitch or a computer game or coaching a team."

Toby had really enjoyed this conversation with Wise Bear. For the first time ever he felt enthusiastic about maths – he was amazed at just how much maths was involved with football.

He even started to wonder how far in metres he could kick a ball, but then he suddenly remembered he had to finish his maths before football training.

"Thank you, Wise Bear," said Toby as he quickly went back to the kitchen table to finish his homework.

It only took Toby 15 minutes to finish his homework, which meant he was in time for football training. He had a great time at training that day, and he played really well.

Later the following week, Toby had a maths test at school and he used his lesson with Wise Bear to help him with a couple of the questions on angles.

He imagined himself kicking a football which helped bring some of the questions to life.

It was the most enjoyable maths test that Toby had ever done! And ever since his chat with Wise Bear, he's enjoyed maths lessons much more.

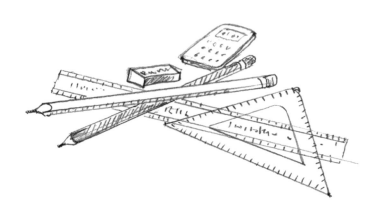

Wise Bear Affirmation: What you say to yourself can
make a big difference to how you think.
That's why Wise Bear always recommends an
affirmation to help you remember his stories.
Here is today's one...

"I am a genius and I apply my wisdom."

(If the idea of referring to yourself as a genius
makes you uncomfortable just know that every
person has a unique set of skills and that they
possess genius qualities within that skill. Read
'Discovering Your Own Uniqueness')

Wise Bear recommends repeating these
affirmations regularly. You can say them either
out loud or inside your head.

Wise Bear exercise:

Use the question below to discuss with your children and family how Wise Bear thinking can help you.

Link something that is not important to you and that you struggle with and ask how doing this activity will help you with something that is important to you and that you love doing.

Here is one example to start you off:

Not important to me	What is important, and I love doing?	How doing what I don't like could help me with what I do like.
Cleaning my room	Drama and singing	I can practise my singing and acting lines while I clean

Not important to me	What is important, and I love doing?	How doing what I don't like could help me with what I do like.

Not important to me	What is important, and I love doing?	How doing what I don't like could help me with what I do like.